Acknowledgement

Many thanks to the engraving work done by the final year students of the **Republic Polytechnic of Singapore:** *David Chew Ho Tin, Ng Yan Bo, Lim Gui-Er Evelyn, Ng Yi Ning Evangeline,* with the guidance of *Mr Ng Ting Hsiang* and project co-ordinated by *Leon Foo.* The kind assistance in editorial work by *Chua Siew Joo, Kellerine Quah, Amanda Foo* and *Tan Yi En* from **Josephine Koh Music Studio.**

All copyrighted works in this collection are produced under license with print permission granted by the following publishers.

Acknowledged with special thanks to :

Keyin Mayhew Limited

Faber Music Limited

Spartan Press Music Publishers Limited

Oxford University Press

Chester Music—Music Sales Group

TEACHERS' CHOICE, SELECTED PIANO REPERTORY

(contains ABRSM examination pieces of 2013-2014 syllabus)

Edited and annotated by Josephine Koh

CONTENTS

Editor's Preface i

Grade 1

Pieces

A1	**W. A . Mozart**	Minuet in G, K. le	1
A5	**Purcell**	Prelude: from *Suite No. 1 in G*	2
A6	**Wagenseil**	Courtly Dance.	3
B4	**Borodin**	Polovtsian Dance: from Prince Igor, (arr. Gritton)	4
B5	**Gurlitt**	Die Klappermühler	5
B6	**F. Wohlfahrt**	Allegretto	6
C4	**Elias Davidsson**	The Merry Bagpipe: from *The Gift of Music*	7
C5	**Heather Hammond**	Cowboy Lullaby: from *Even Cooler Piano*, Book 2	8

Studies

1	**Josephine Koh**	Easy Moving Bass	9
2	**F. Wohlfart**	Slurs and Staccatos	10
3	**F. Wohlfart**	Light Staccatos for Both Hands, Op. 35	11

Grade 2

Pieces

A3	**T. Attwood**	Allegro:1st movement from Sonatina No. 2 in C	13
A4	**Duncombe**	Giga	15
A5	**Handel**	Menuett in G minor, BWV 453/4	16
A6	**Haydn**	Minuet in B flat (arr. Hall)	17

B5	**Glinka**	Polka	18
B6	**Sullivan**	Gavotte: from The Gondoliers (arr. Hall)	19
C4	**Julian Anderson**	Somewhere near Cluj	21
C5	**David Blackwell**	Cat's Eyes, arr. Hall	23

Studies

1	**Müller**	Melody and Legato Playing	25
2	**C. Czerny**	Double Notes, Op. 823	26
3	**C. Czerny**	Contrasting Articulation in Both Hands, Op. 823	27
4	**C. Czerny**	Triplet Accompaniment in the Left Hand, Op. 23	28

Grade 3

Pieces

A1	**C.P.E Bach**	Allegro in G, H. 328	29
A4	**W.F. Bach**	Allemande (arr. Hall and Harris)	30
A6	**L. Mozart**	Menuet in A. No. 12 from L. Mozart, *Notebook for Nannerl*	31
B5	**C. Mayer**	Study in C, Op. 340 No. 1	32
B6	**Swinstead**	In the Bay	33
C5	**Brian Chapple**	Blues: from *Lazy Days*	35

Studies

1	**Josephine Koh**	Rhythmic Exercises	36
2	**Loeschhorn**	Finger Articulation	37
3	**Kirchner**	Staccato with Precision	38

Editor's Preface

This compilation is drawn from authentic sources, with suggested editorial suggestions for teaching and learning purposes. I would recommend that teachers assist students to find for themselves, the best approaches to meet their physical and musical abilities.

Pedagogical points are provided on what constitutes acceptable performance practice, which would include articulation, pedaling and tempo. As musical understanding and stylistic practices evolve with time, the approach in this collection serves to meet students' needs while preparing for the ABRSM examinations. Musical perspectives concerning tone, sound, articulation, and dynamics may vary in different cultural and social contexts. With various sensibilities highlighted in the explanatory notes, teachers may find it helpful when facilitating their students' imagination and technique. When in doubt, I would highly recommend that original or Urtext scores be consulted.

Fingering
They are suggestive and in no way to be conformed. Good fingering is important. Decide on what works best based on:

(i) efficient facilitation of fingers that would help establish fluency in the playing.
(ii) the natural weight of each finger that would project a good sound and tone quality.
(iii) good, relaxed muscular control on the whole; over the hands, fingers and joints

Metronome markings
Most are suggested speeds to suit the mood and character of the pieces.

Articulation
Most baroque and classical works contain editorial suggestions which reflect the stylistic practices of the periods. These articulations, however, are often varied by different performers.

Dynamics and performance directions
Additional editorial suggestions are indicated in brackets or below the scores.

Pedal Marks
Pedaling has been indicated in detail in most instances. Harmony plays a determinant role in making decisions on pedal changes. Special effects, stylistic features and other considerations based on the mood of a piece may require the use of the pedal in an unconventional manner. At higher grades, pedaling technique often becomes more demanding, which often contribute to the overall effect of a piece. In most cases, a musical performance requires good footwork and a sensitive ear to achieve the intended effects.

Josephine Koh

Editorial Symbols

The editorial symbols used throughout this series are explained below.

	Slurred notes, to be played *smoothly*. They are usually found in original scores and sources.
	Dotted slurs are editorial marks which suggest that the notes are to be played *smoothly in one musical direction.*
	Long dotted lines indicate suggested *phrasing,* usually 2, 4 or 8 bars.
✓	This mark is used to indicate a *point of breath,* more significant than the end of a phrase.
I	The note is be held to its *full value* but *separated* from the next. This creates a non-legato effect.
(3 1 2 4)	An *alternative* set of fingering suggested.
	Pedal mark suggests the movement of the foot.
	This suggests the use of *non-legato pedaling.*
	This suggests the use of *legato pedaling*. The pedal change is made after the next note is sounded.
	The dynamic marking is editorial, i.e. not notated in the original sources.

Grade 1
A:1

Minuet in G

This piece is a simple dance, very suited to the young. The counterpoint between both hands has to be well co-ordinated. Played with well curved fingers and clear articulation, this delightful minuet with regular phrases is structured to feature elegant dynamic contrasts. It is important to ensure that a good lift is given to the quaver couplets. One should not give an undue accent onto the first down beat of every 2-bar phrase.

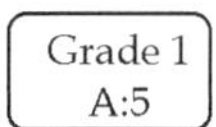

Prelude

from *Suite No. 1 in G*

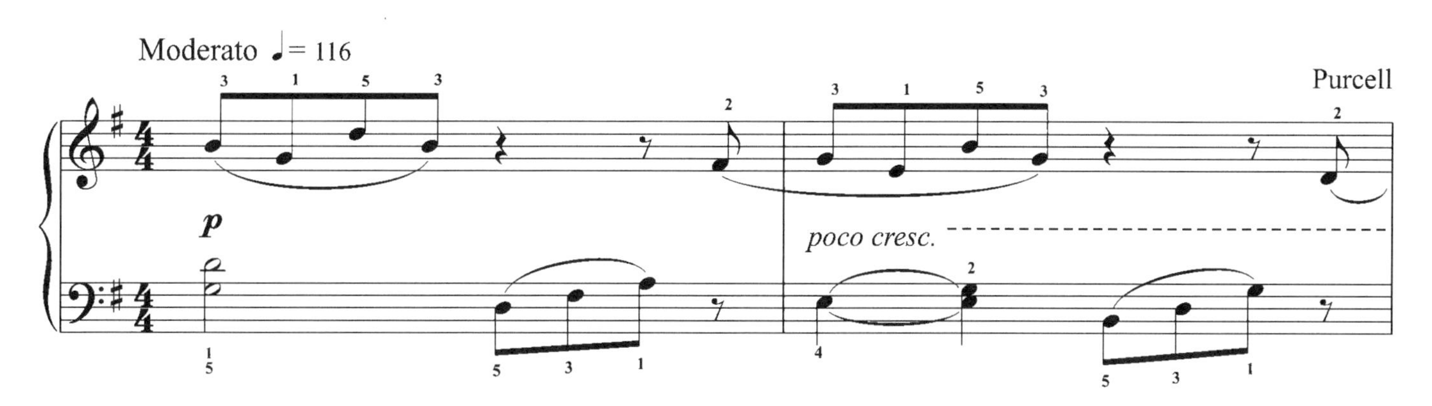

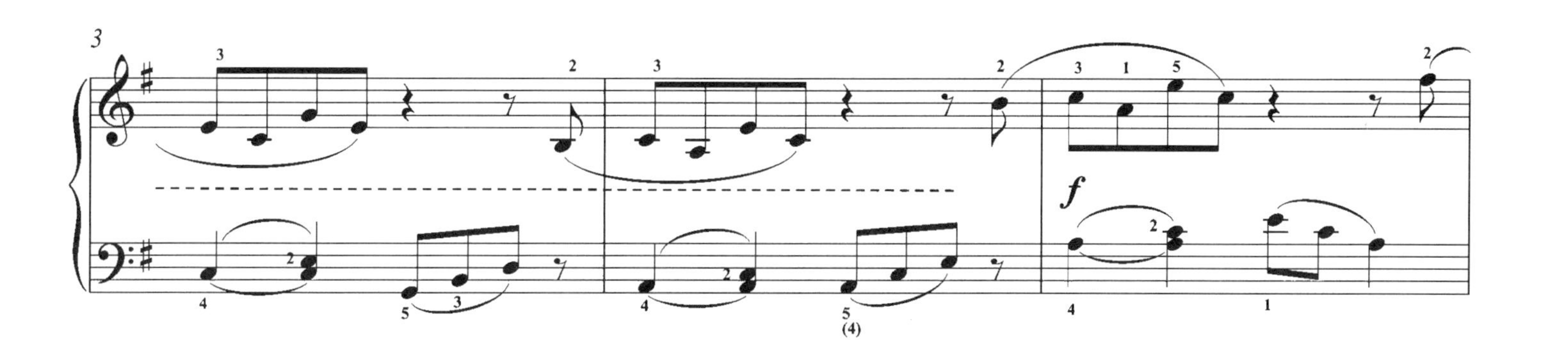

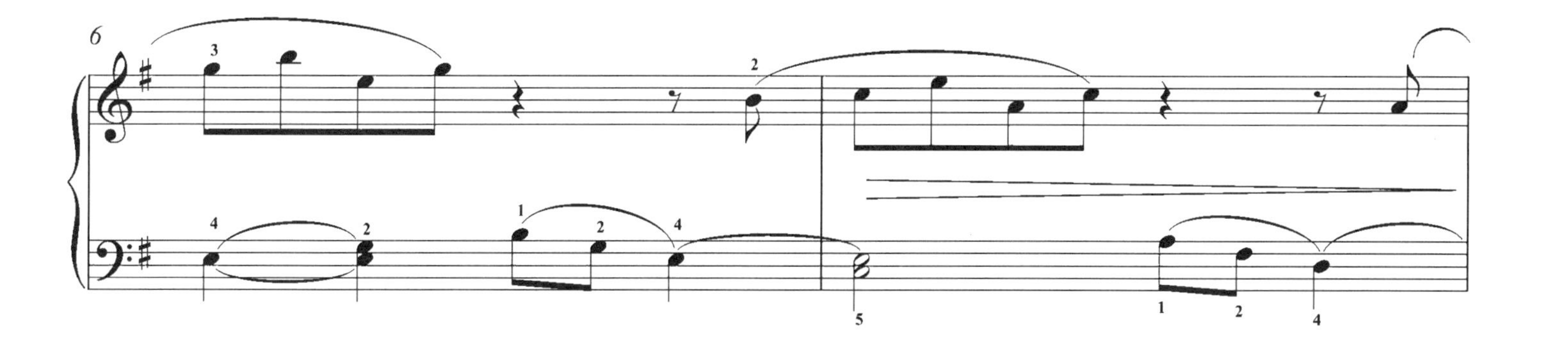

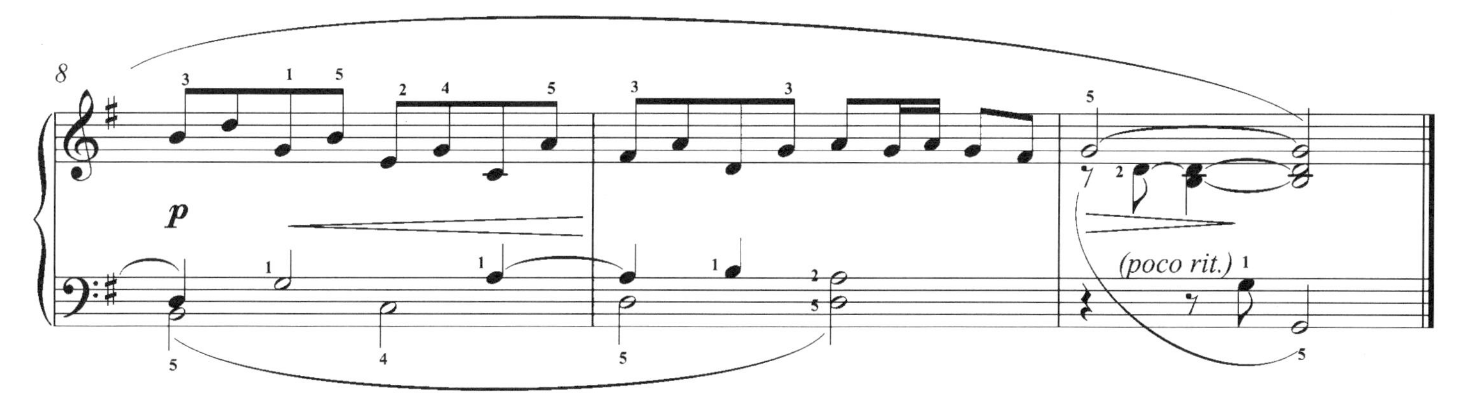

The melody is built on simple broken chords, recurrent in every bar with the left hand responding. The style is elegant, with good legato touch and shape needed. The last phrase requires more fluency, to be played with sound fingering and held notes in the left. A good sense of melodic shape would express this short piece effectively.

Grade 1
A:6

Courtly Dance

Andantino grazioso ♩ = 116-126

G.C. Wagenseil

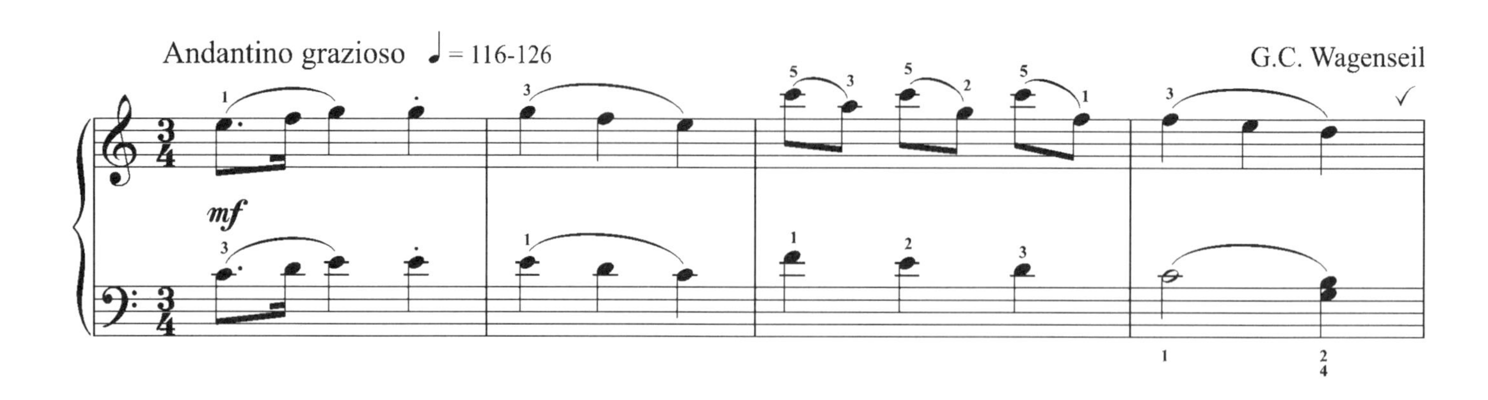

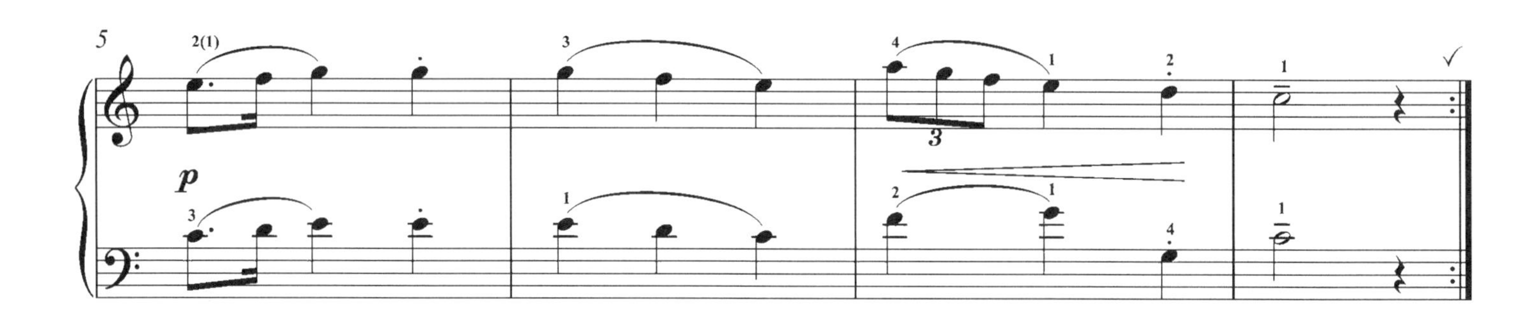

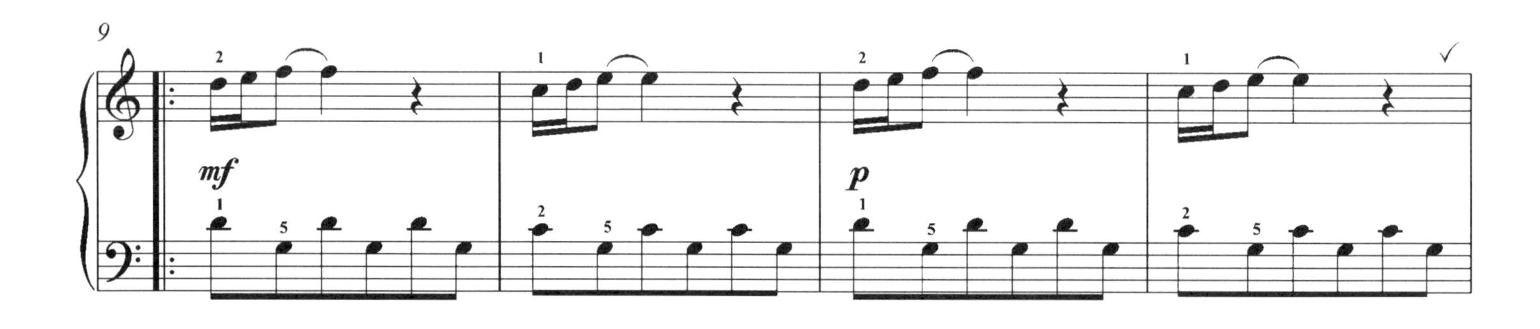

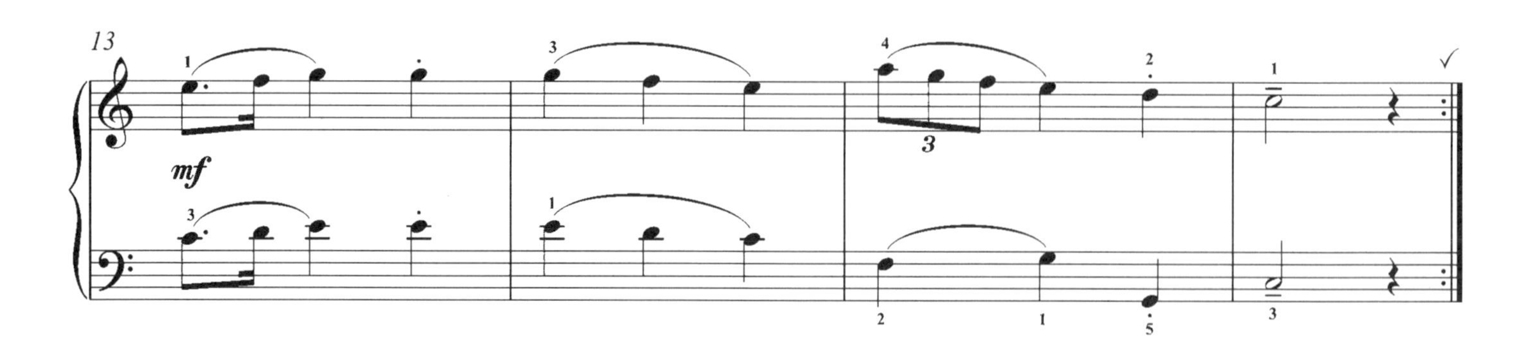

This courtly dance has to be played with well coordinated hands, along with precise finger work and tonal control. The touch should never become too heavy for the best effect. The dotted rhythm needs a graceful approach, without sounding crisp, even with staccato notes. This piece is in a simple dance style of which a constant pulse should be kept throughout.

Grade 1
B:4

Polovtsian Dance

This famous Russian melody from the opera Prince Igor has an exotic and charming character. The left hand accompaniment must be kept quiet in the background with a very smooth melody above it. An expressive and singing touch, with some weight from the right arm would help to bring out the phrases. The last note of each phrase needs to be lifted off elegantly. The bass notes of the concluding bars are to be played softly. Do make sure that both hands are well co-ordinated at all times.

Grade 1
B:5

Die Klappermühle

No.33 from The First Lessons, Op.117

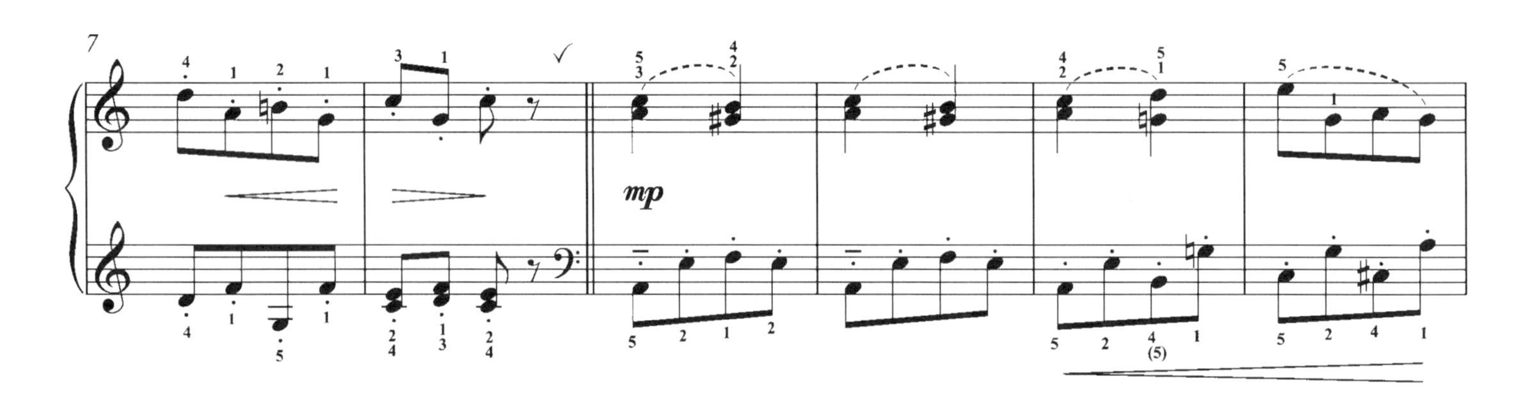

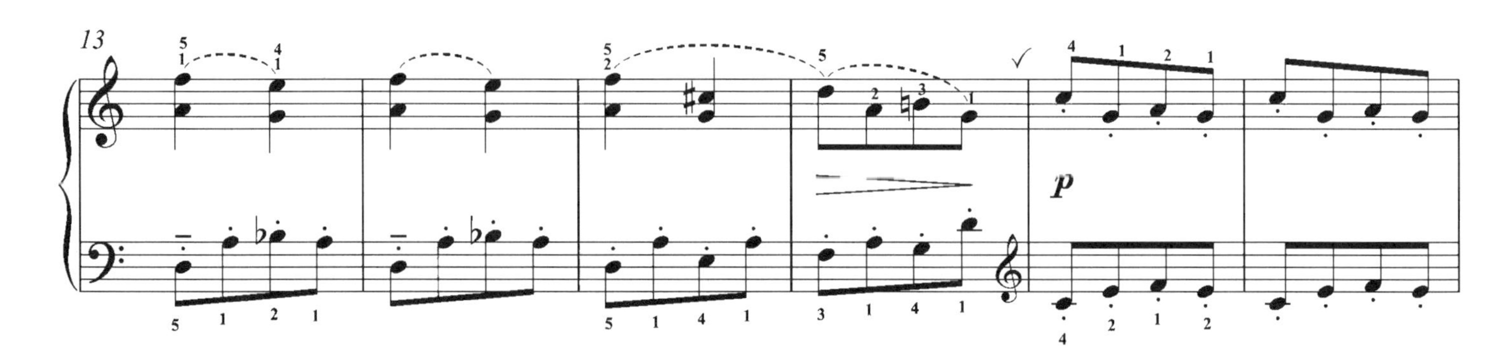

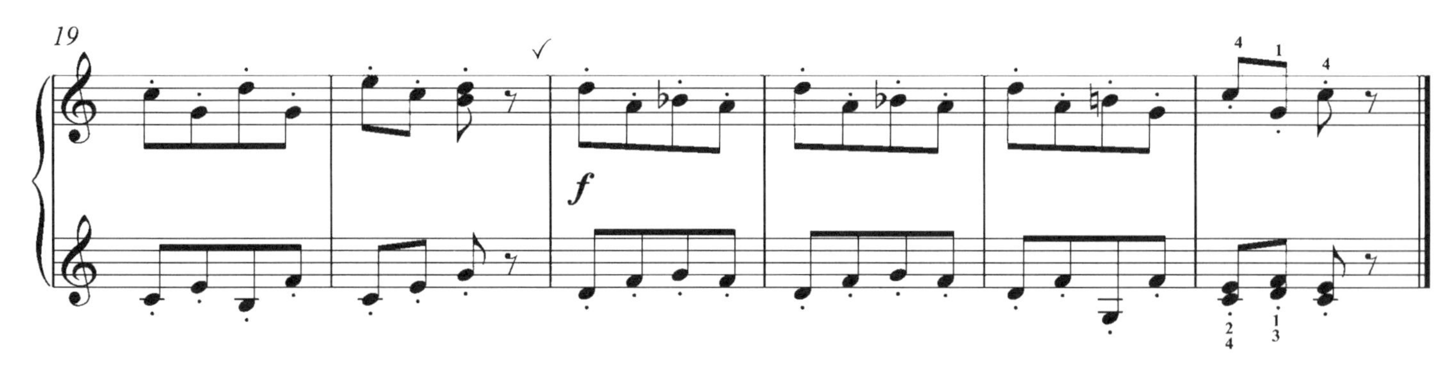

This piece is almost a study in staccato touch. Firmly curved fingers, played with a precise metronomic pulse would achieve a rather impressive effect. The first beat of each bar requires a somewhat deliberate accent to kick off the 2/4 metre. It is important to observe the dynamics and the relatively quick tempo to achieve the humorous effect.

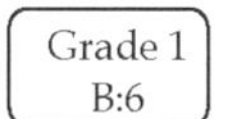

Allegretto

F. Wohlfahrt

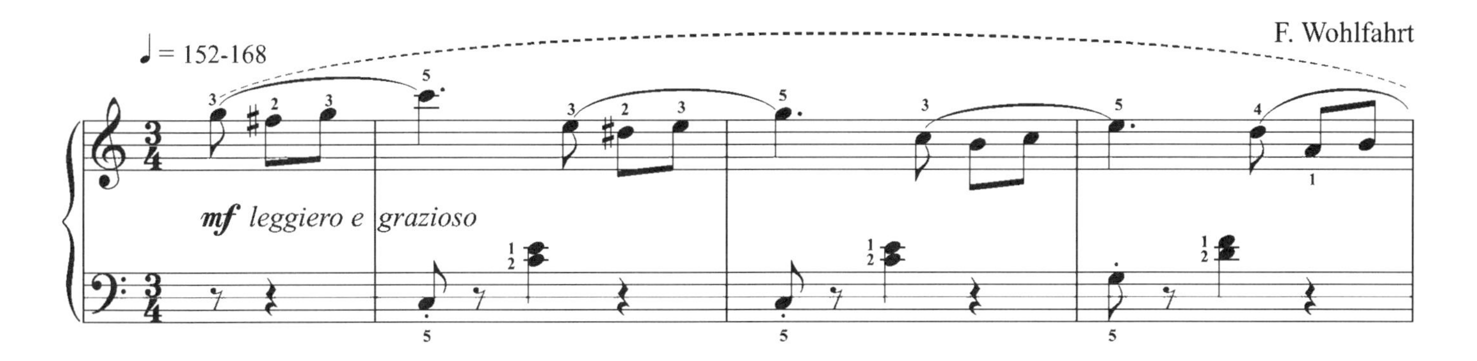

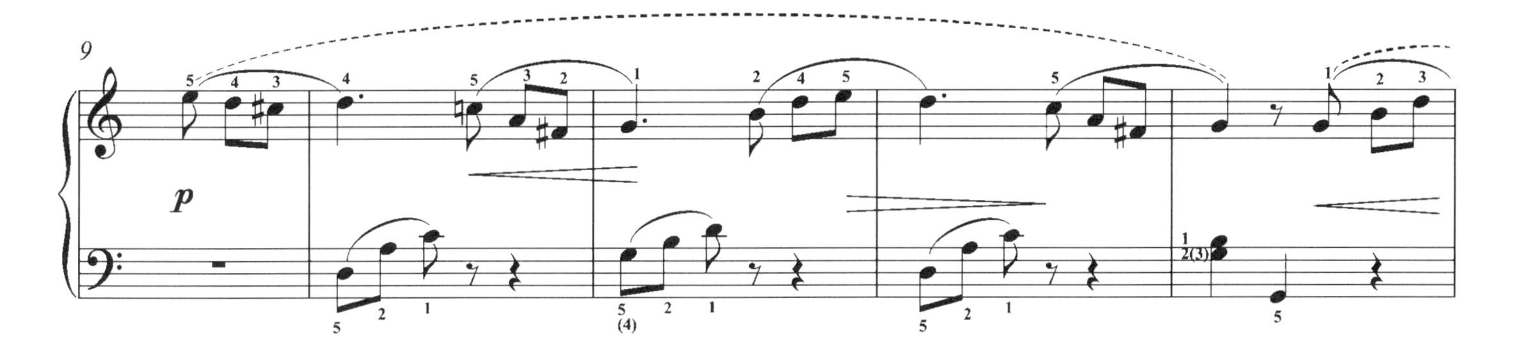

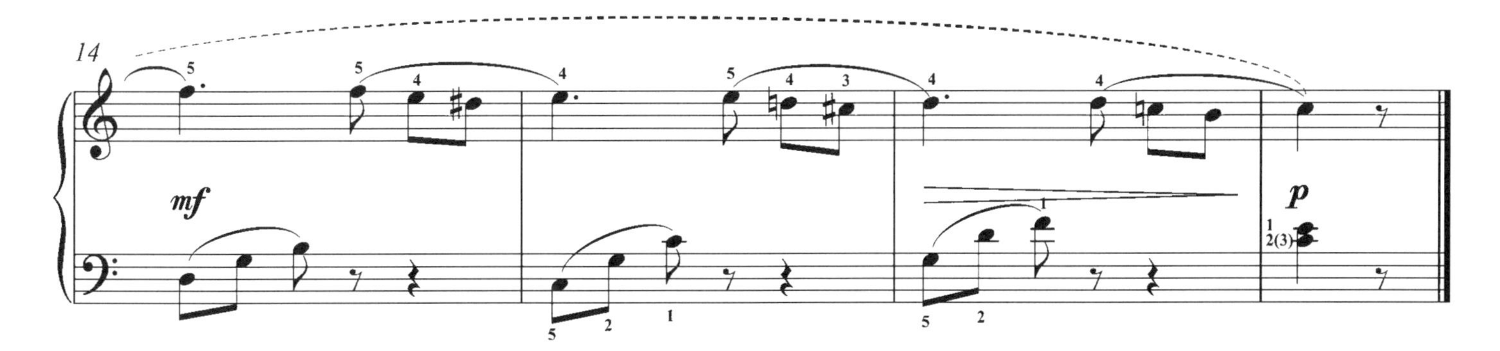

This piece has a charming character. The right hand takes off with a bright, cheerful melody which descends with sequences for the first two phrases. The accompaniment in the left hand first calls for emphasis on the second beat. From bar 10, the mood changes, with softer dynamics and a smoother broken chord pattern in the left hand. The dotted crotchet in the right hand should not be accented, but placed with good weight from the finger and then slurred with an upward motion of the wrist. The melody should always be played with the left hand kept at a softer hue.

Grade 1
C:4

The Merry Bagpipe

from *The Gift of Music*

Elias Davidsson

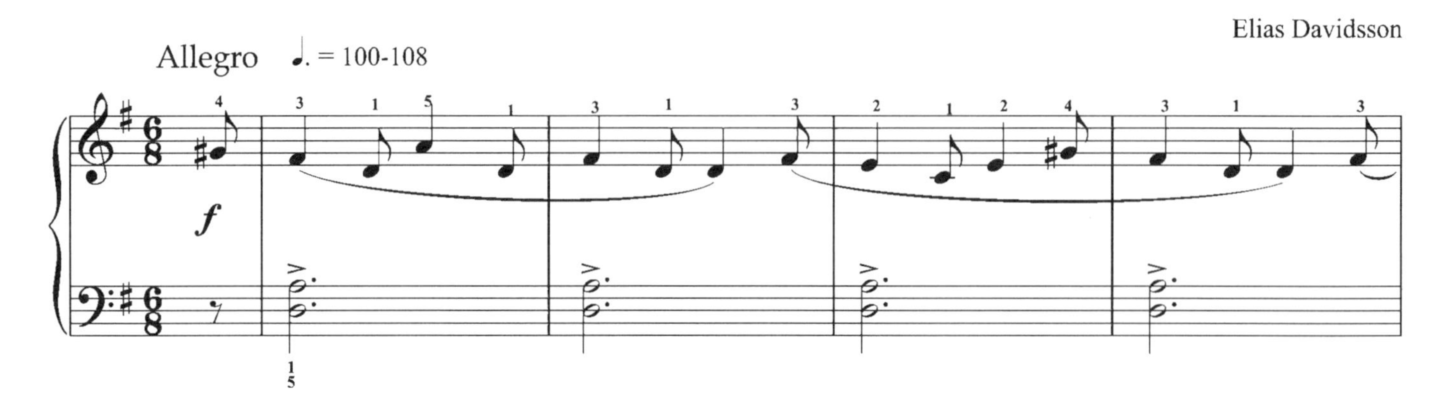

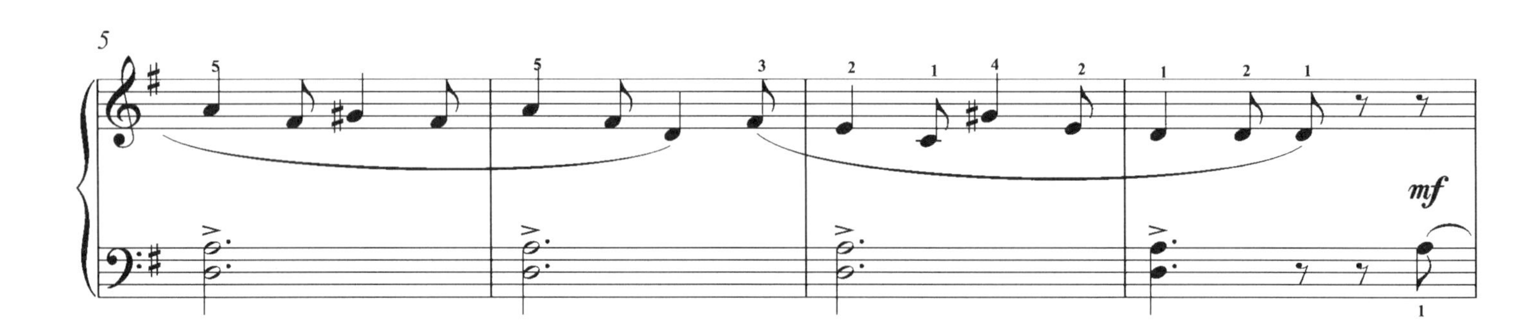

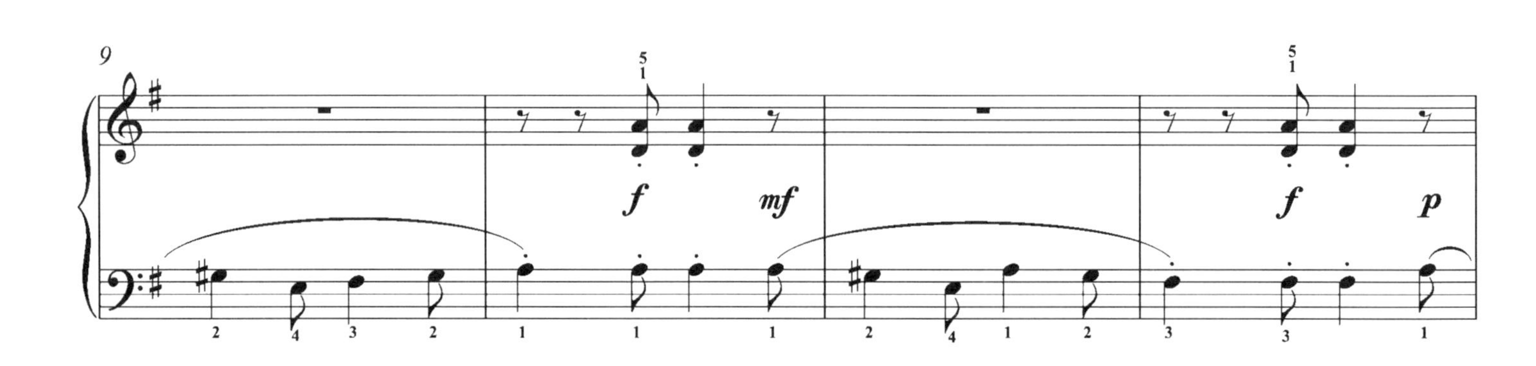

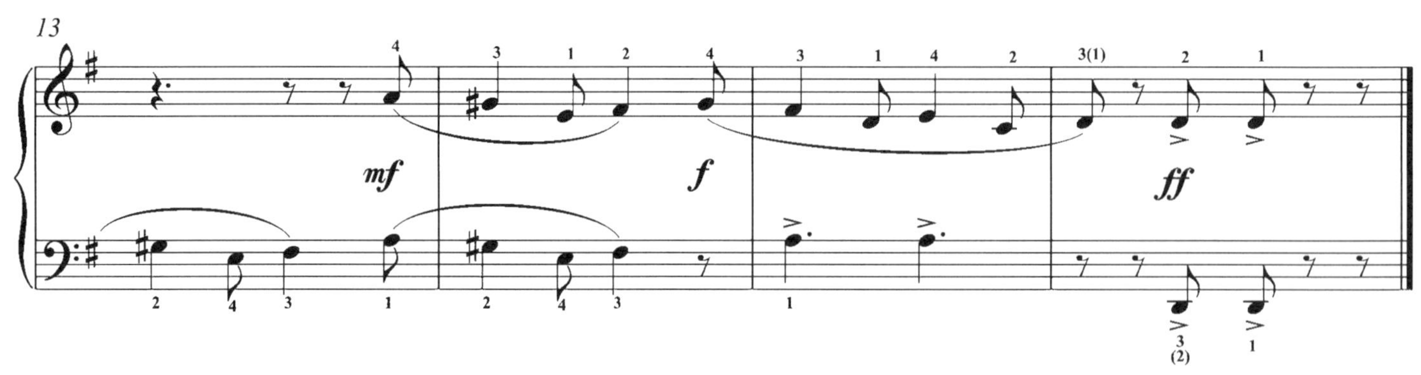

This is an energetic and vibrant piece of which the drone in the left hand of the first 8 bars should be played accented. The melody features the modal, exotic effect of bagpipe music, with detached chords that provide rhythmic interest in bars 10 and 12. The piece is not difficult, though co-ordination between both hands has to be precise to achieve the intended effect. Most students will be thrilled to play this spirited piece.

Grade 1
C:5

Cowboy Lullaby

from *Even Cooler Piano, Book 2*

Drowsily ♩. = 66 (In a slow rocking style)

Heather Hammond

This piece is recommended for Grade 1 students with larger hands that are required to hold the bass notes rhythm. The general mood is relaxed, as the cowboy rocks to sleep. With a legato left hand that repeats the accompaniment with different chord structures, the melody would take off well with a deep mellow tone, with the cowboy nodding off to sleep. The left hand may be played with an undulating effect, subtly

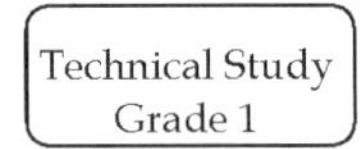

Easy Moving Bass

adapted by
Josephine Koh

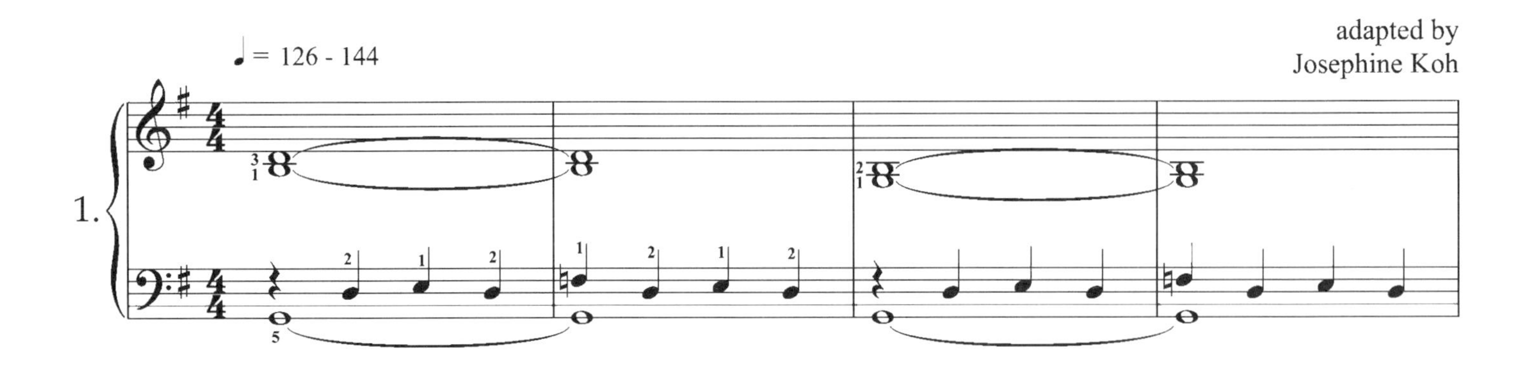

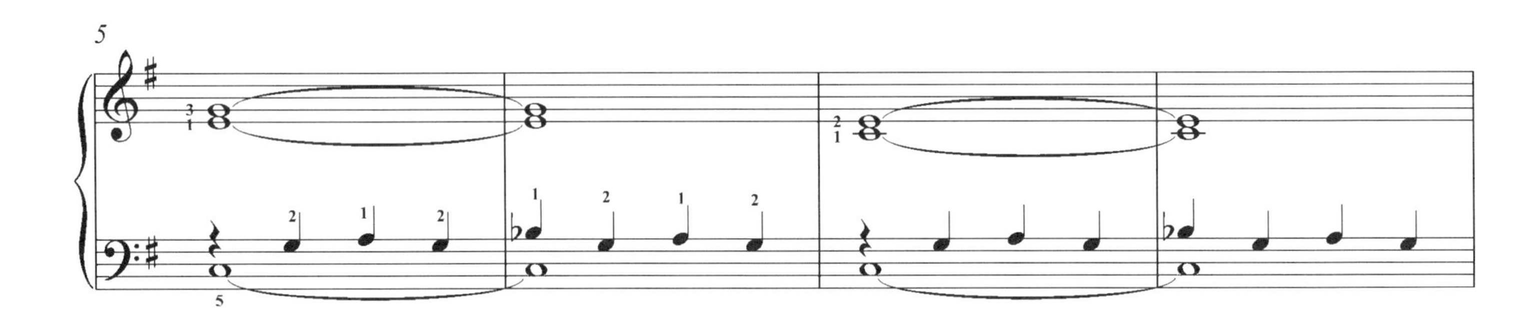

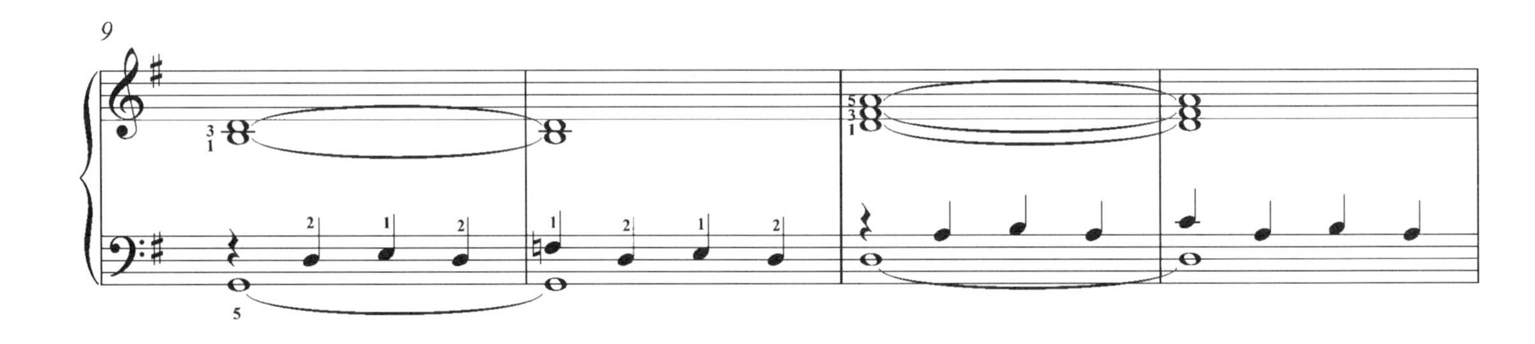

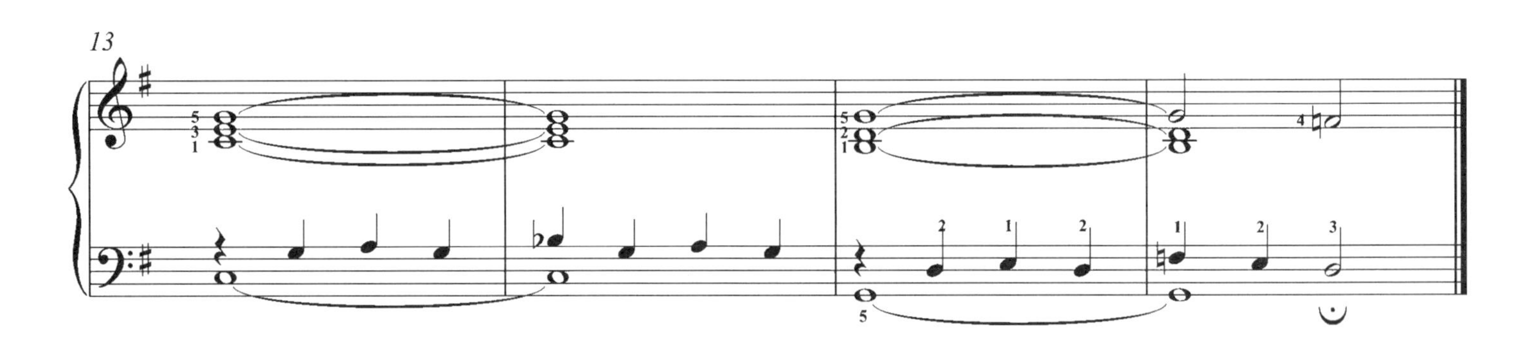

This study serves as a preparatory exercise to the examination piece Grade 1, C5 (Heather Hammond's Cowboy Lullaby). Once the student has worked through the bass part here, it would be much easier to proceed to learn the piece.

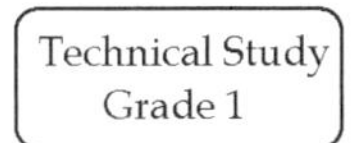

Slurs and Staccatos

Op.36, No. 18

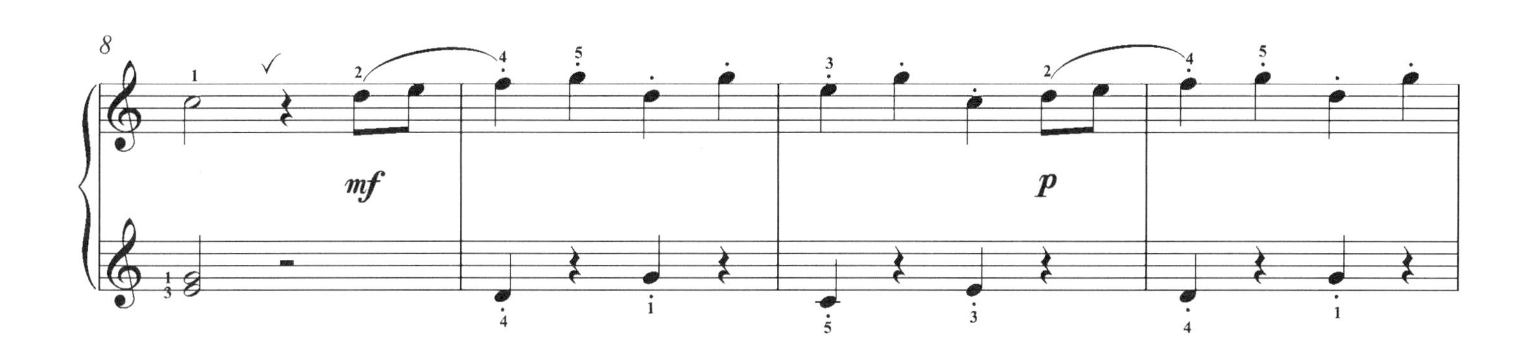

A study in mixed articulation and staccatos, this short piece is effective to ensure good co-ordination between both hands. It is certainly a great study piece as well as repertoire for the early grade student.

Technical Study
Grade 1

Light Staccato for Both Hands

Op. 36

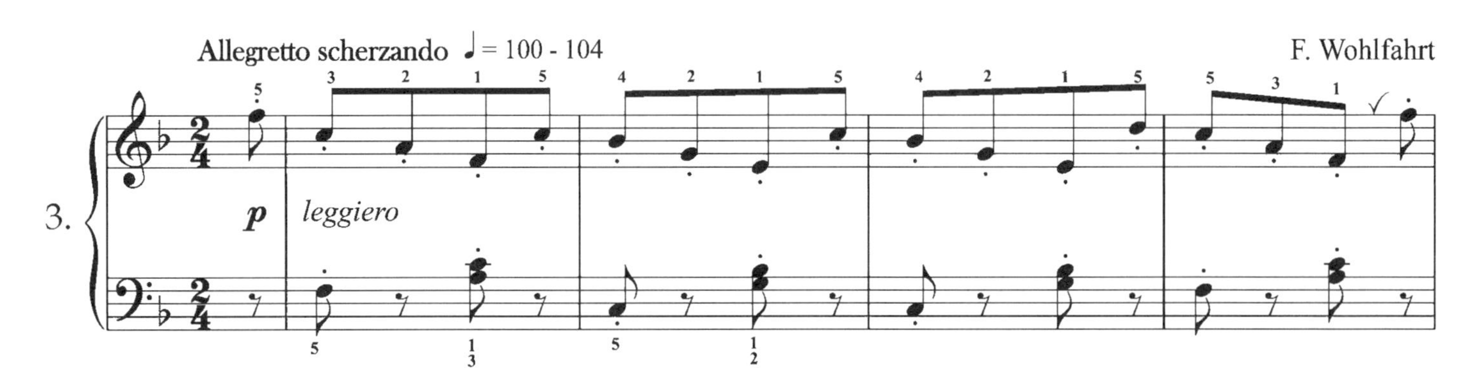

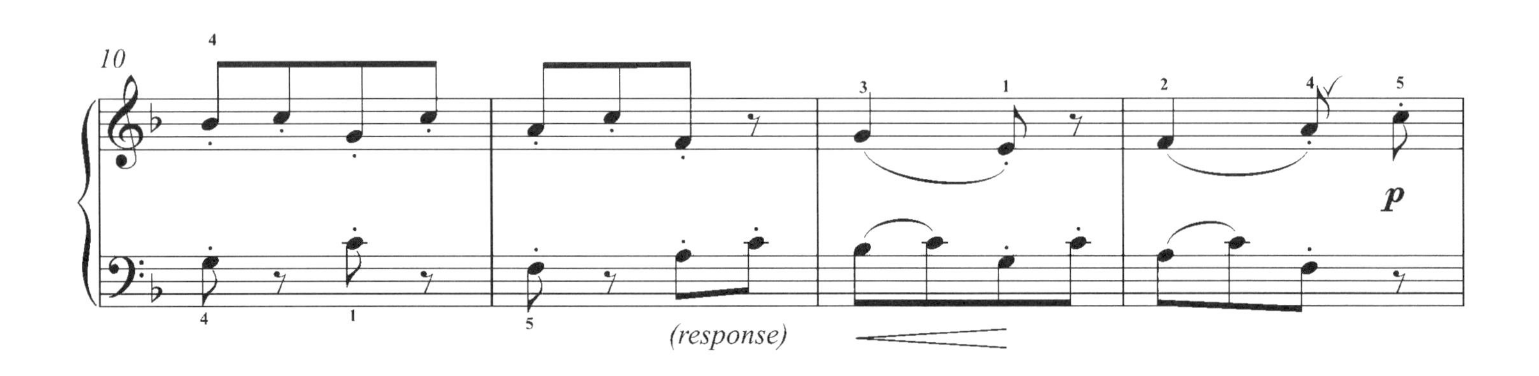

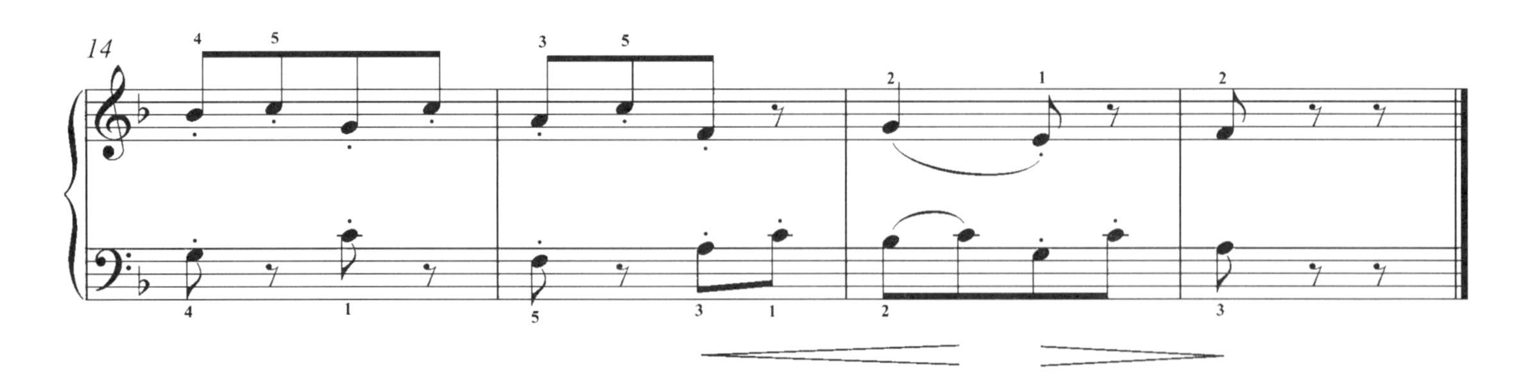

Simply a study on staccato playing, the fingers need to be firmly and clearly articulated. It is important to ensure that good finger staccato is achieved with a steady tempo and evenness in the control. The fingering has to be learnt, particularly with the leaps between notes.

Blank Page

Grade 2
A:3

Allegro

1st movt from Sonatina No.2 in C

This sonatina movement is lively and cheerful. The repeated right hand notes in the melody are best articulated differently – slurred, detached, held. With the regular phrasing, musical interest can be brought about with changes in dynamics. Co-ordination between the hands may prove to be a challenge for young students.

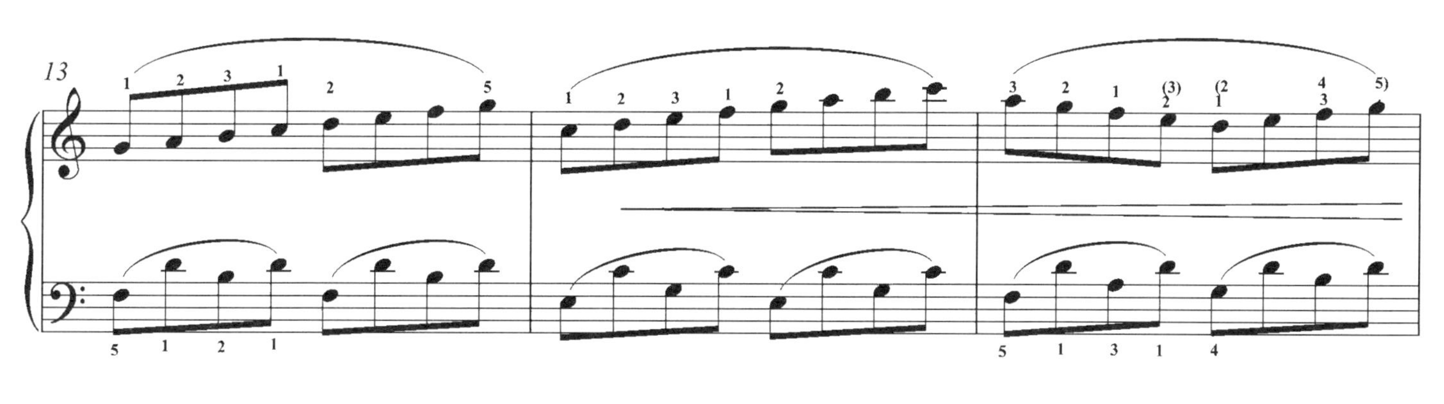

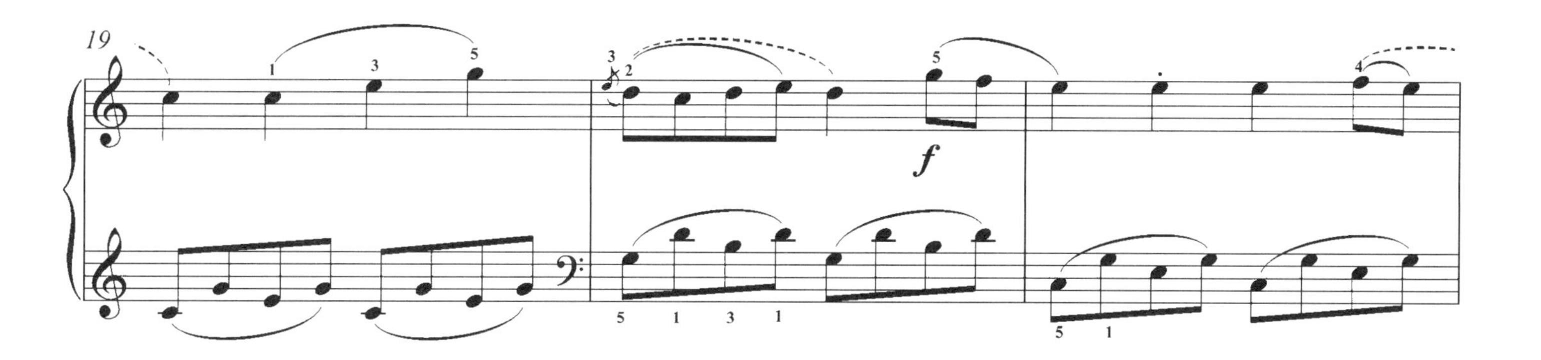

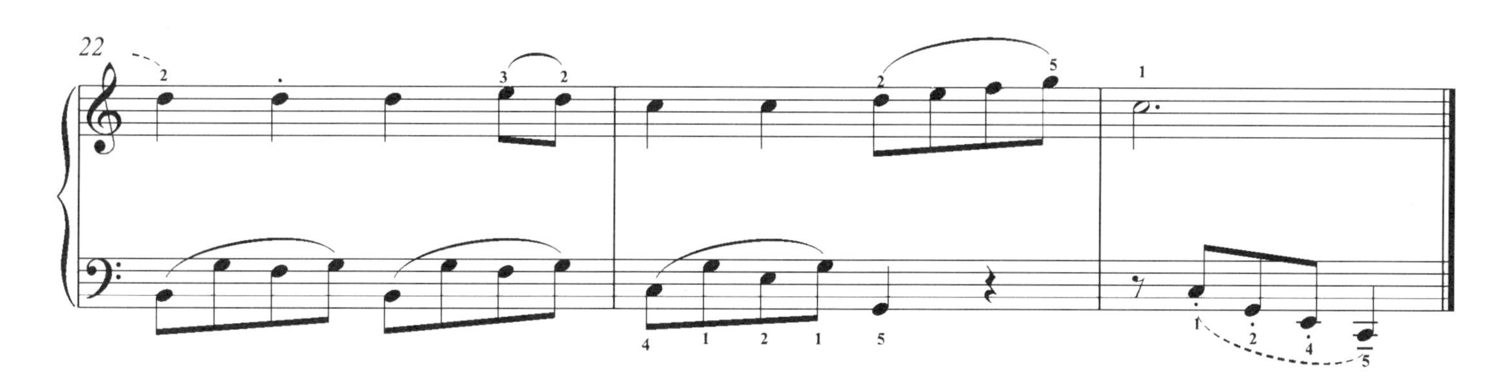

From bars 9 to 16, particularly with scale passages in one hand and alberti bass accompaniment in the left hand, it is best that each hand is practised separately. It is important to maintain a steady tempo with the left hand being subdued to the melody.

Grade 2
A:4

Giga

This dance-like piece has a simple 4-bar phrase structure. The dotted crotchets in 6/8 time create a swing effect, along with the short trill that should not be played too heavily or quickly. An elegant approach is most appropriate for the grace notes. Dynamic contrasts with clear dainty articulation for detached notes would portray the light-hearted spirit of this piece effectively.

Grade 2
A:5

Menuett in G minor

HWV 453/4

The key of G minor is dark and somewhat saddens this minuet. The touch, with the thirds in the right hand, should be firmly depressed for a non-legato sound. At bar 9, there is an assertive tone in the right hand as the music moves to the higher register. Quavers need to be well connected with evenness in the rhythm. A consistent crotchet beat ought to be kept throughout, which would express the melancholic character of the piece.

Grade 2
A:6

Minuet in B flat

This classical minuet opens confidently approach with f. The bright melody in B flat major takes off with the left hand playing in counterpoint from bars 1 to 4. The second phrase has a cheerful character, with rolling broken chords and a leaping melody. From bar 7, the second section contrasts with smooth triplet quavers in the right hand before ending the piece with a firm perfect cadence. Technically, the triplets from bars have to be played evenly. Students need to study the finger carefully to ensure fluency in bars 7 to 9.

Polka

Grade 2
B:5

This quick polka in D minor is a steady Russian dance with an accent on the 2nd beat of every two bars. The melody has a rustic effect and somewhat narrow in range. However, the left hand accompaniment, which should be kept lighter than the right hand creates the stamping movements of folk music. Thus, the staccato articulation needs to be clearly contrasted with the slurred dotted rhythms and legato semiquavers in the right hand.

Grade 2
B:6

Gavotte

from *The Gondoliers*

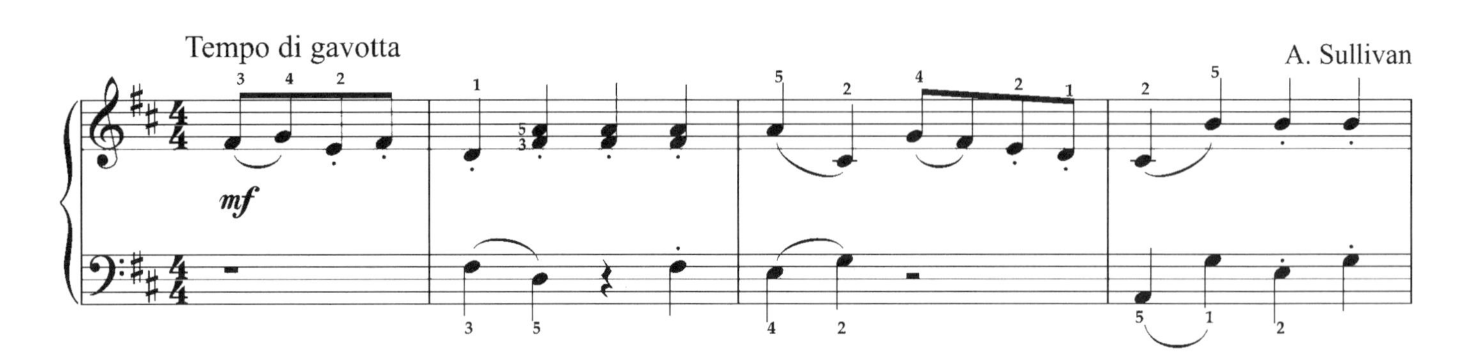

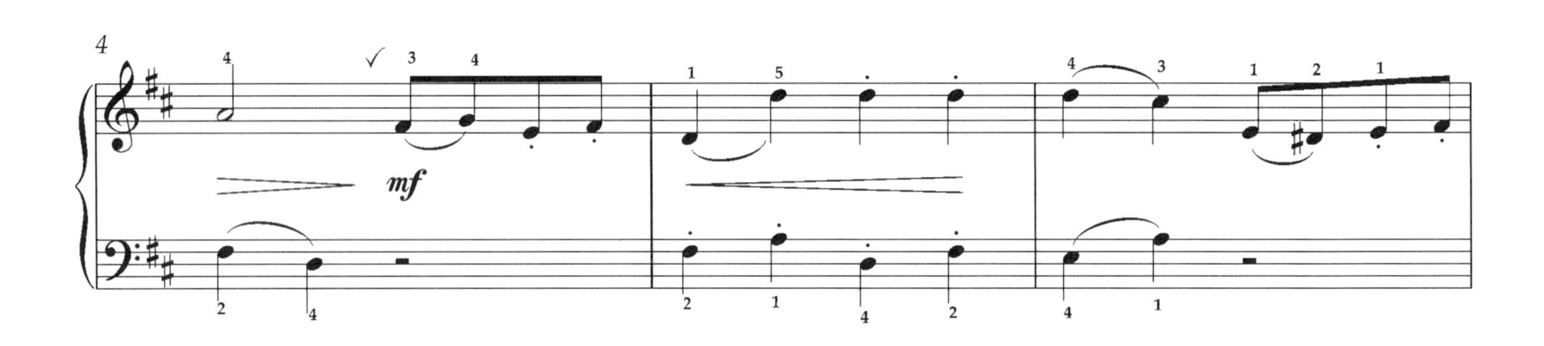

This gavotte, a dance adapted from Sullivan's opera The Gondoliers, is simple and light-hearted. It has a childlike charm that entertains at a moderate tempo. It is possibly difficult for students to manage the staccatos in both hands with use of short slurs. Nevertheless, the melody is very attractive, with a narrative element. Some dynamics have been suggested to provide more interest to the piece.

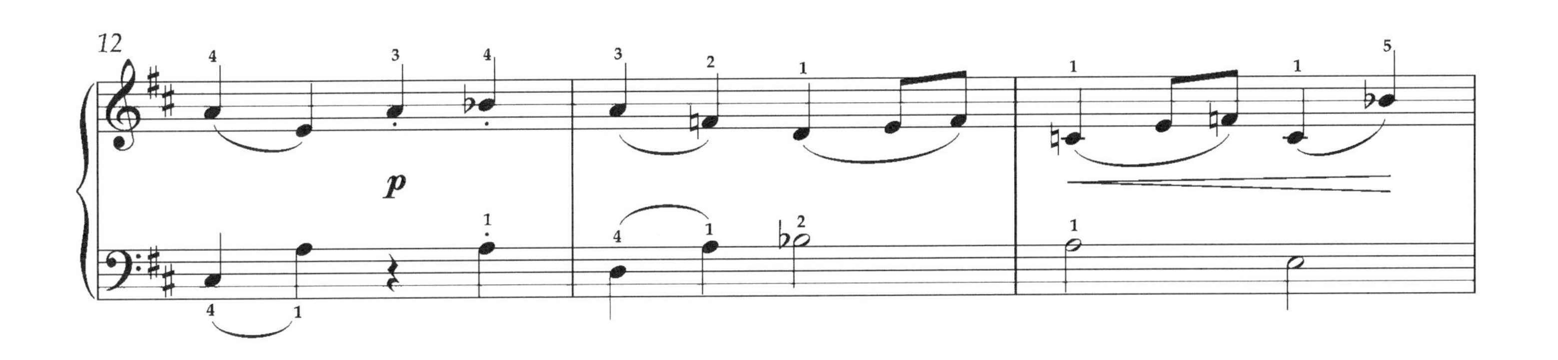
12
p

15
mf

18
mp

21
f

Grade 2
C:4

Somewhere near Cluj

The composer writes, "This piece uses a simple, folk-type melody, somewhat reminiscent of the traditional music found in the region of Cluj in Romania". The modal melody, slow and repetitive, is to be played quietly, yet singing in an expressive manner. It has an imaginative and pastoral mood. A good legato touch is required with some pressure exerted on the fingers. The accompanying part has to be kept light, that would certainly blend well, when played with good control and balance with the melodic part.

Grade 2
C:5

Cat's Eyes

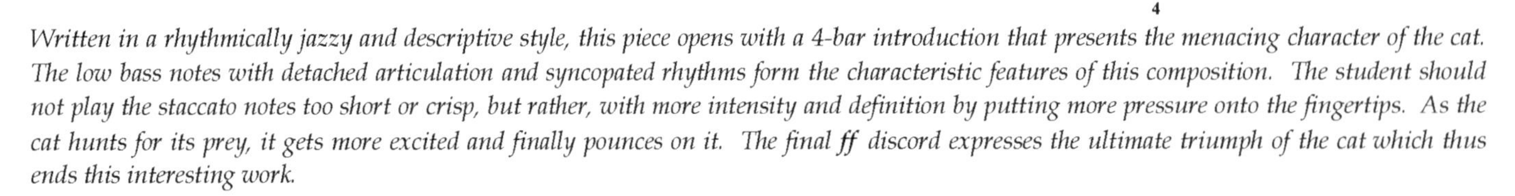
Written in a rhythmically jazzy and descriptive style, this piece opens with a 4-bar introduction that presents the menacing character of the cat. The low bass notes with detached articulation and syncopated rhythms form the characteristic features of this composition. The student should not play the staccato notes too short or crisp, but rather, with more intensity and definition by putting more pressure onto the fingertips. As the cat hunts for its prey, it gets more excited and finally pounces on it. The final ff discord expresses the ultimate triumph of the cat which thus ends this interesting work.

17

20
pp
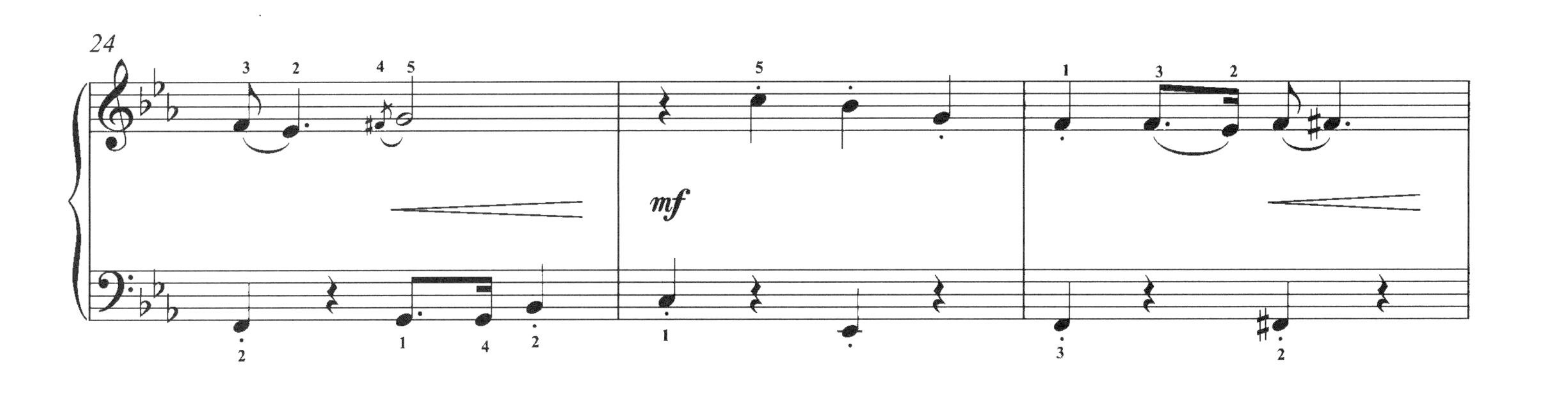
24
mf

27
f
mp
p
ff

Technical Study
Grade 2

Melody and Legato Playing

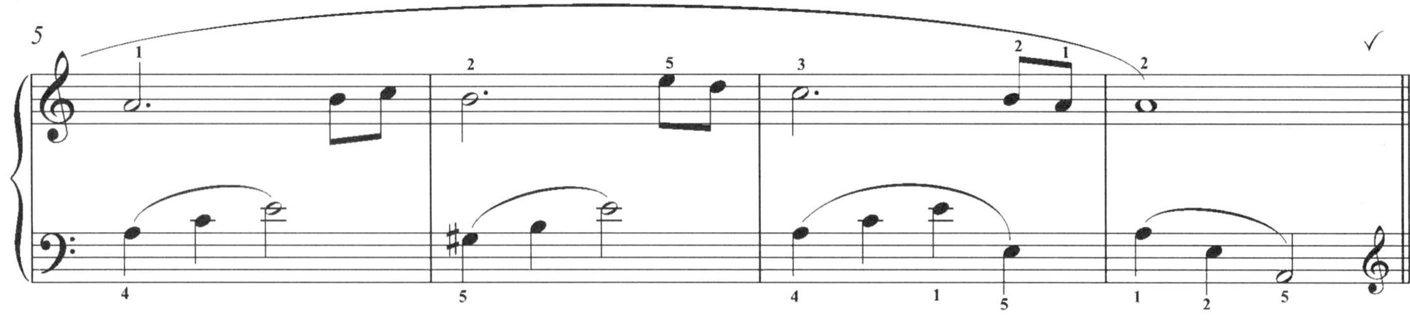

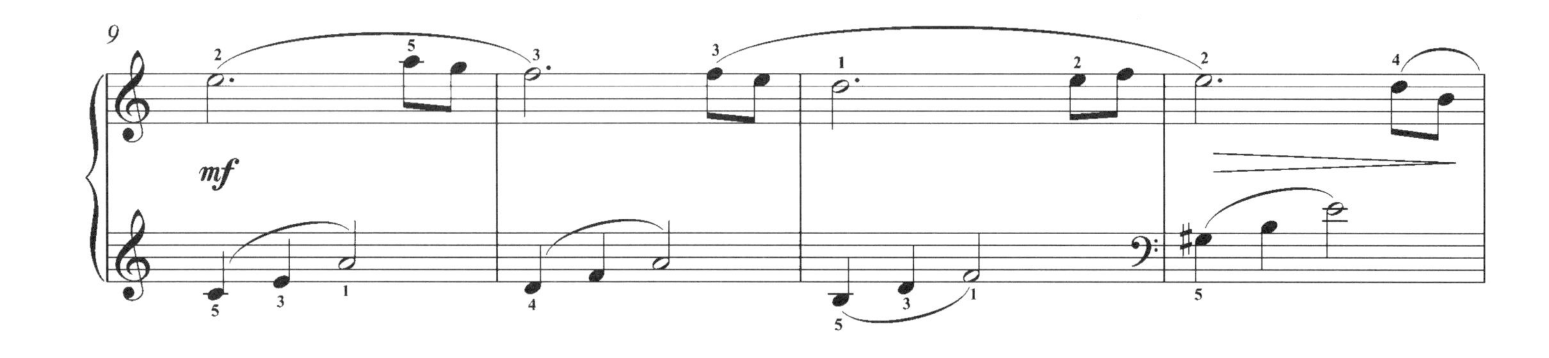

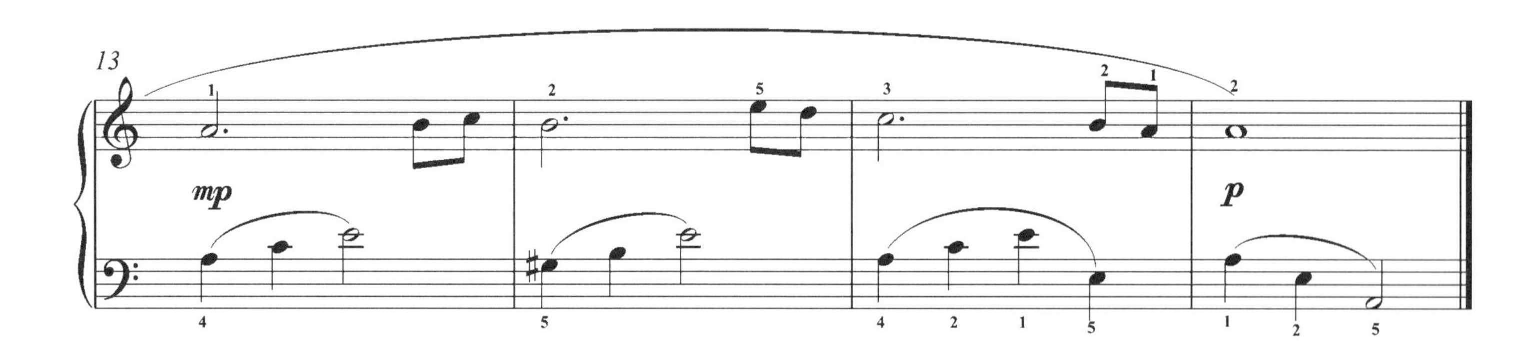

Legato technique has to be developed at a young age. This study features a lyrical melody with long notes and quick movement of quavers on the last beats accompanied by well-shaped broken chord patterns in the left hand.

Technical Study
Grade 2

Double Notes

from *The Young Pianist, Op. 823*

Czerny

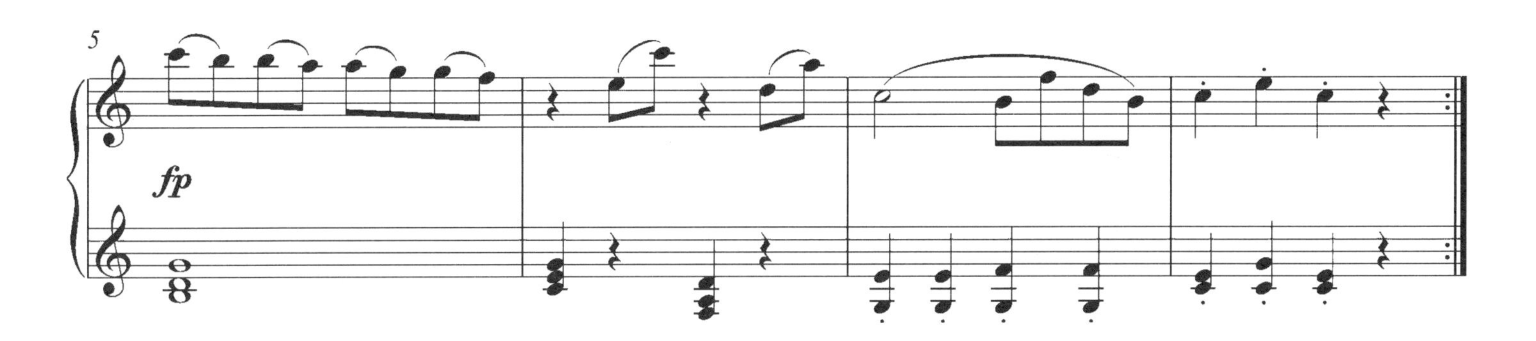

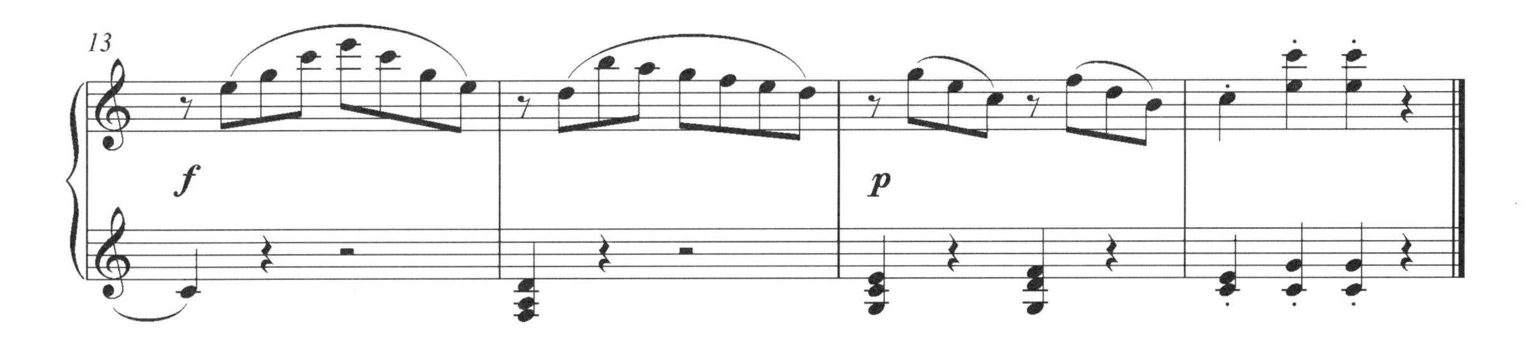

A study for the playing of thirds and slurred couplet, this piece is attractive and simple, being in the key of C major!

Technical Study
Grade 2

Contrasting Articulation in Both Hands

from *The Young Pianist,* Op. 823

Czerny

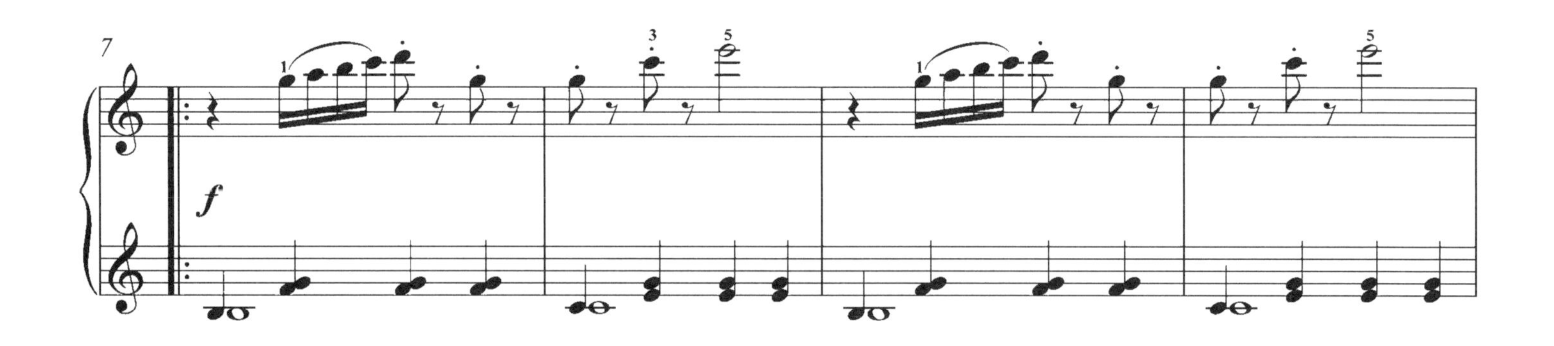

This study is a little challenging for the grade 2 student. However, it is most effective where practice in facilitation of quick finger work is needed. The leap of the octave in the right hand gives the study a cheerful character. The bass notes, to be held in the left hand ensures that the weaker fingers are effectively strengthened.

Technical Study
Grade 2

Triplet Accompaniment in the Left Hand

from *The Little Pianist, Op.23*

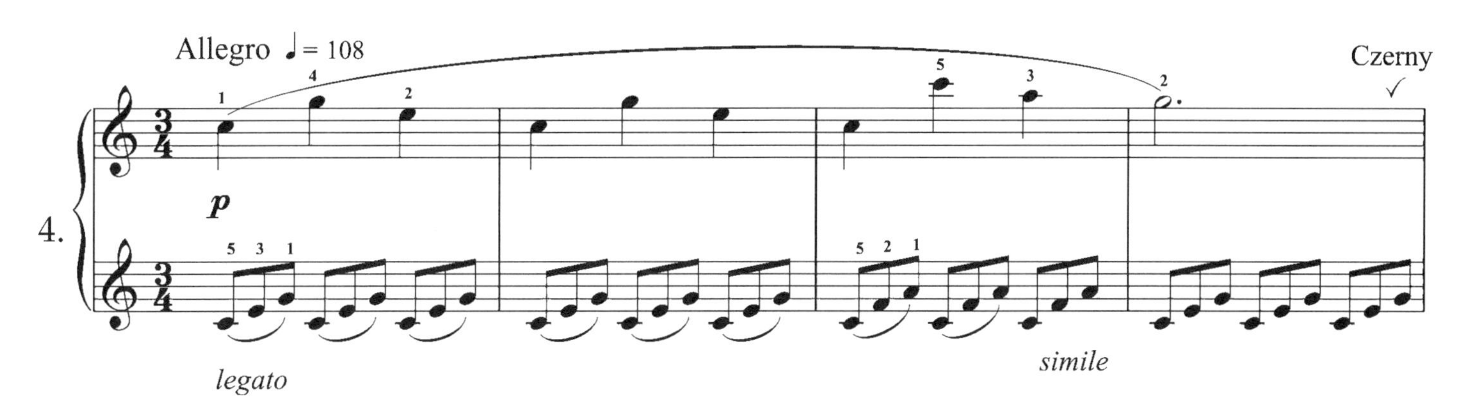

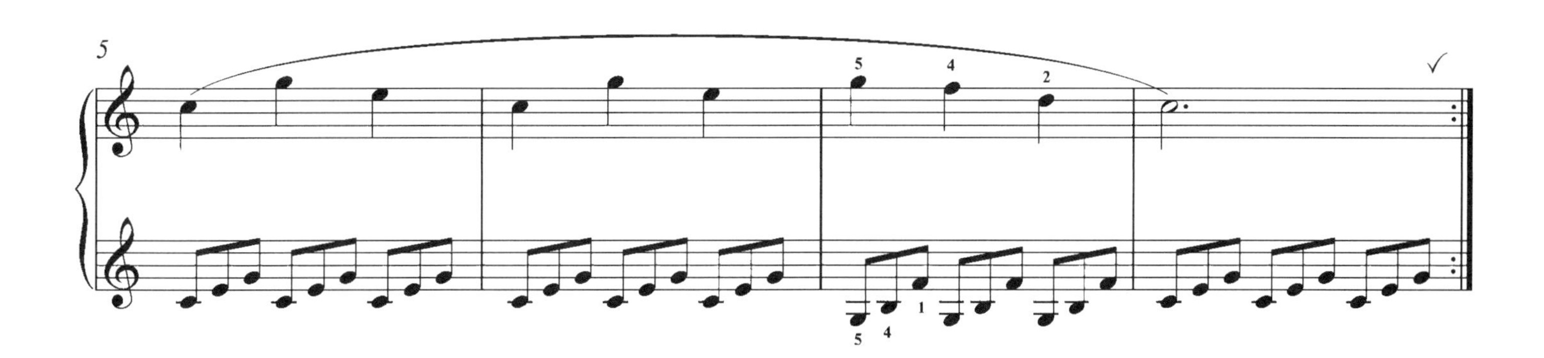

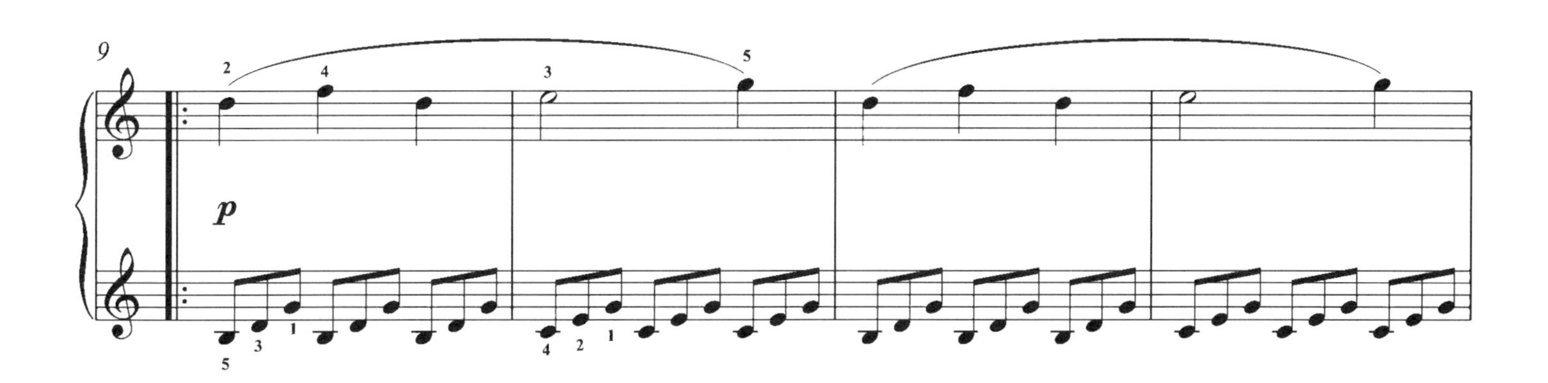

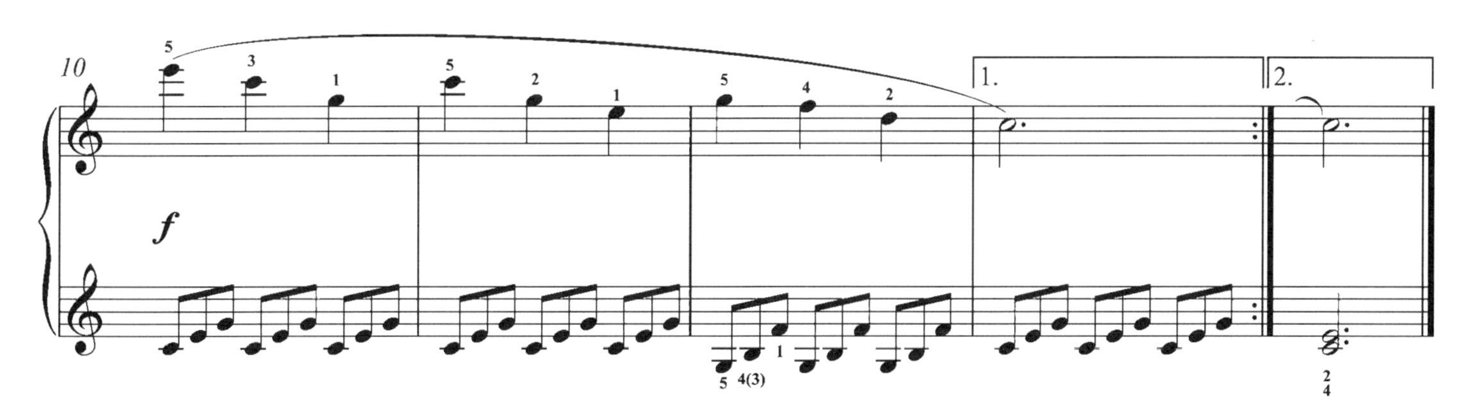

With a number of pieces in the syllabus that requires the playing of triplets. This study would serve the purpose for more practice for the left hand, with a lyrical melody that soars above it.

Grade 3
A:1

Allegro in G

H.328

C.P.E. Bach

Written in two-part counterpoint, this allegro has a lively dance-like character. The melody is bright, which can be effectively attained by good and clear finger articulation. The need for dynamic contrasts and some finer shading in the musical statements define the distinctive characteristics emerging from the pre-classical era. The slurs, staccatos and mixed articulations are editorial, all added for stylistic effectiveness.

Allemande

Grade 3
A:4

A short dance in the melancholic key of G minor, it is an allemande based on a dual texture - a mixed of homophony and 2-part writing. Editorial marks have been provided to assist students with the range of articulation required. A gentle lift would be effective on the upbeat. While it is wise to keep the L.H toned down, the double harmonic notes can be played with a slight accent on the first beat of each bar.

Grade 3
A:6

Menuet in A

No. 12 from *L. Mozart Notebook for Nannerl*

L. Mozart

A simple minuet with balanced 2-bar phrases, this work is written for a young child, by Leopold Mozart. The light dance steps can be felt in the 3/4 rhythms and use of mixed articulation. In ternary form, the lilt of the opening is repeated as the principal musical motif recurs. The use of effective dynamic contrasts and shading would ensure that this is a pleasant and enjoyable piece for the young student.

Grade 3
B:5

Study in C

Op.340 No.1

Mayer

This study has a sweet singing melody which has to be played with a very legato touch. The phrases are to be shaped, along with the delicate changes in dynamics. A steady tempo with a quiet thumb in the left hand for the alberti bass accompaniment is essential. From bars 11 to 16, the passage could be technically daunting. It is wise to practise the hands separately before combining them to achieve a flawless performance.

Grade 3
B:6

In The Bay

This highly expressive mood piece, this has an almost dreamlike setting. A graceful melody is conceived with gradual rise and fall of its contour. The left hand arpeggios have to be played with a flexible wrist that would sink onto the first quaver and lifted off gently on the last. The use of dynamics ought to be gradual, never forceful or too deliberate. The harmonies are extremely suited to the colours of the piece, giving it a tranquil, yet illuminating effect.

The use of the pedal is certainly recommended, but care has to be taken on the release, which needs to be gradual and controlled, but not too slow. At Grade 3, though the use of rubato would somehow be advanced, the natural flow of the beautiful sounds calls for a relaxed approach. This piece is highly recommended for the musical student.

Grade 3
C:5

Blues
from *Lazy Days*

The crotchet pulse in the left hand establishes the character and mood of this jazz piece in the opening bar. A regular tempo has to be maintained throughout despite the swing rhythms of the melody in the right hand. The acciaccaturas and chromatic notes within the dotted rhythms create much interest and it would be an interesting work for those looking to play something relaxing and entertaining.

Technical Study
Grade 3

Rhythmic Exercises

No. 1 (repeat each exercise at least 5 times, beginning at a slow tempo and with increasing speed)

Josephine Koh

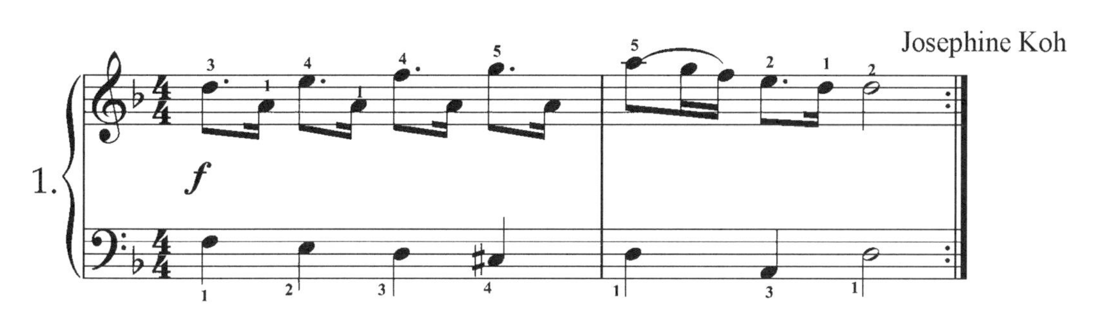

No. 2

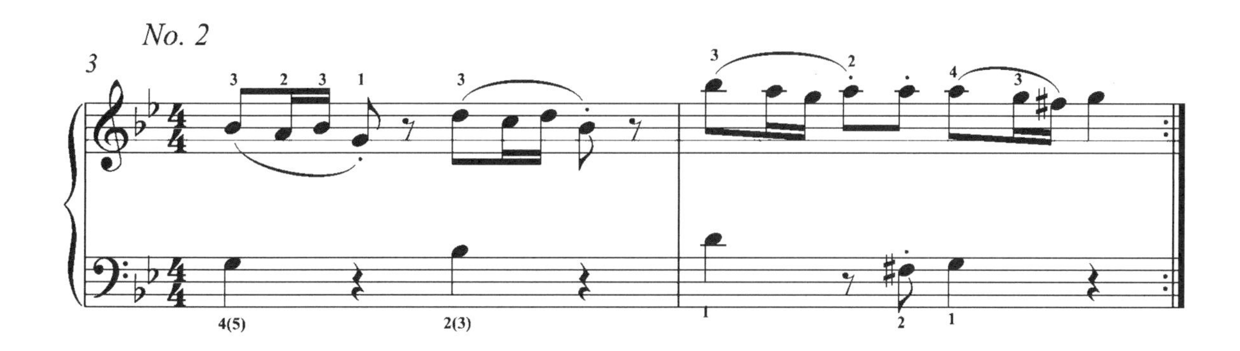

No. 3

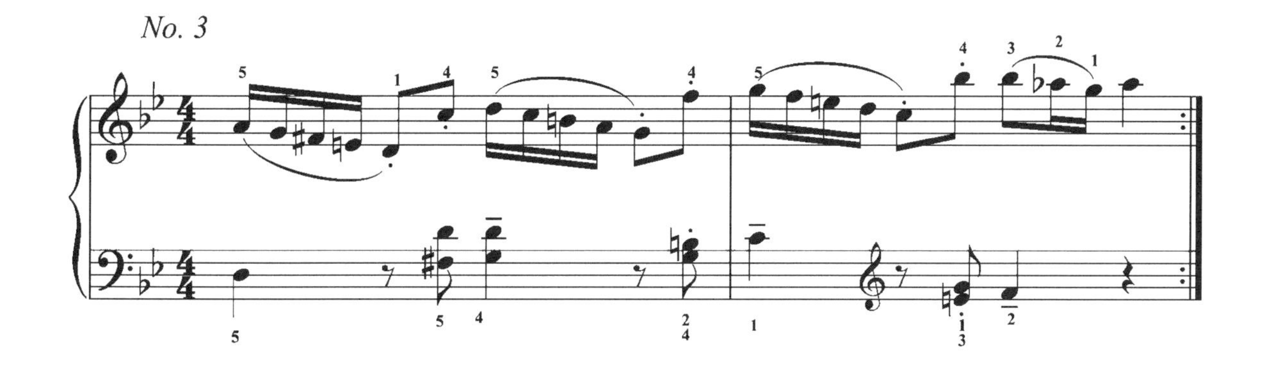

No. 4

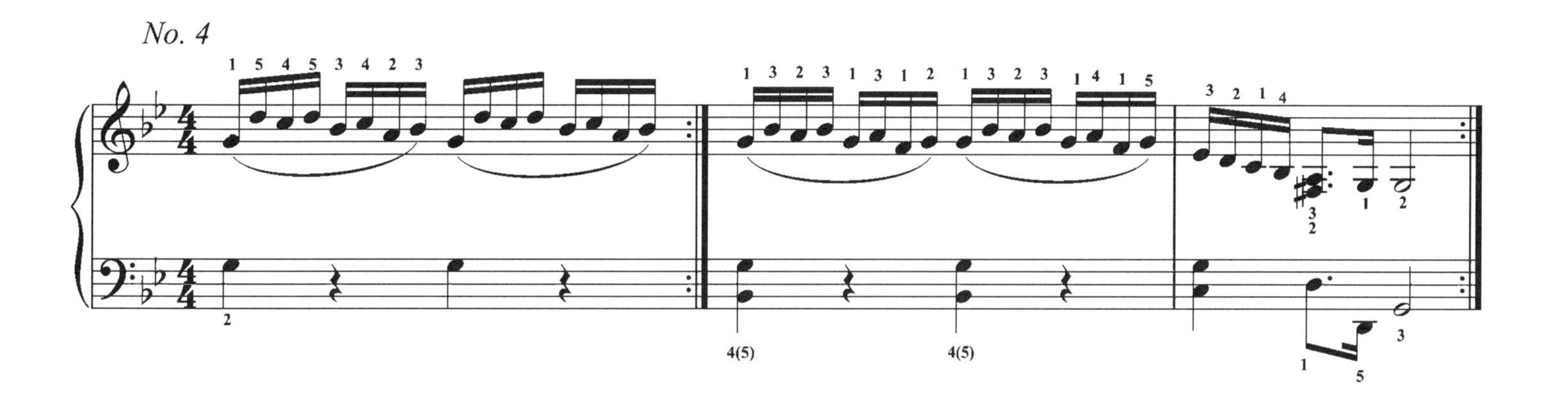

This study is effective for those who would look to develop a sound finger technique for runs and scalic passages. The melodic motif in bars 5 to 8 are commonly found in classical piano works. The fingering patterns should thus be learnt and adhered to.

Technical Study
Grade 3

Staccato with Precision

Op.71 No. 11(Extract)

Best-Selling Titles

Scales and Arpeggios for Piano (Grades 1 to 8)
J Koh's Fingering Method

Students can now learn scales and arpeggios in the most enjoyable and effective way. *J Koh's Fingering Method* develops the learners' cognitive skills by using a combination of visual, auditory and tactile systems. Now available in print, this proven method used for training gifted children is specially produced to assist students prepare for the ABRSM graded piano practical examinations. Success assured! The series from Grades 1 to 5 focuses on establishing good fingering habits. The *Fingering & Tonality Method* for Grades 6 to 8 continues the development of technical competence in piano students based on key and chord structures.

Practice in Music Theory (Grades 1 to 8)
Revised Edition
by Josephine Koh

The revised edition of the *Practice in Music Theory* series is a set of highly recommended instructional workbooks for students who wish obtain a sound foundation in music theory. The *J Koh's* teaching approach is academic and logical, yet musically conceived. Progressive topics are set out to guide students through their understanding of the fundamental musical concepts and ideas. Based on the requirements of the ABRSM theory syllabus, this series has :

- clear teaching points and graphical illustrations
- explanatory notes that are applied throughout the series
- exercises of progressive difficulty that provide students with sufficient practice to master the topics and concepts learnt
- updated information and study notes that are most effective for reference and revision.

Rhythmatics
by Josephine Koh

Group notes, write beats, identify time signatures and complete bars with missing notes or rests — all these tasks with ***Rhythmatics***, the most sought after musical learning aid for young children. Attractive colour cards, each with a particular colour and shape corresponds to a specific time value. With the cards to be arranged on the base whiteboard mathematically, the child visualises the concept instantaneously and is able to perceive the number of beats in a bar. Most suitable for children between ages of 4 to 9, ***Rhythmatics*** is recommended for the study of music theory up to Grade 2.